Arna and Ruby
Friendships and School

An Autism Graphic Novel

Written by
Helen Eaton

Illustrated by
Kris Coley

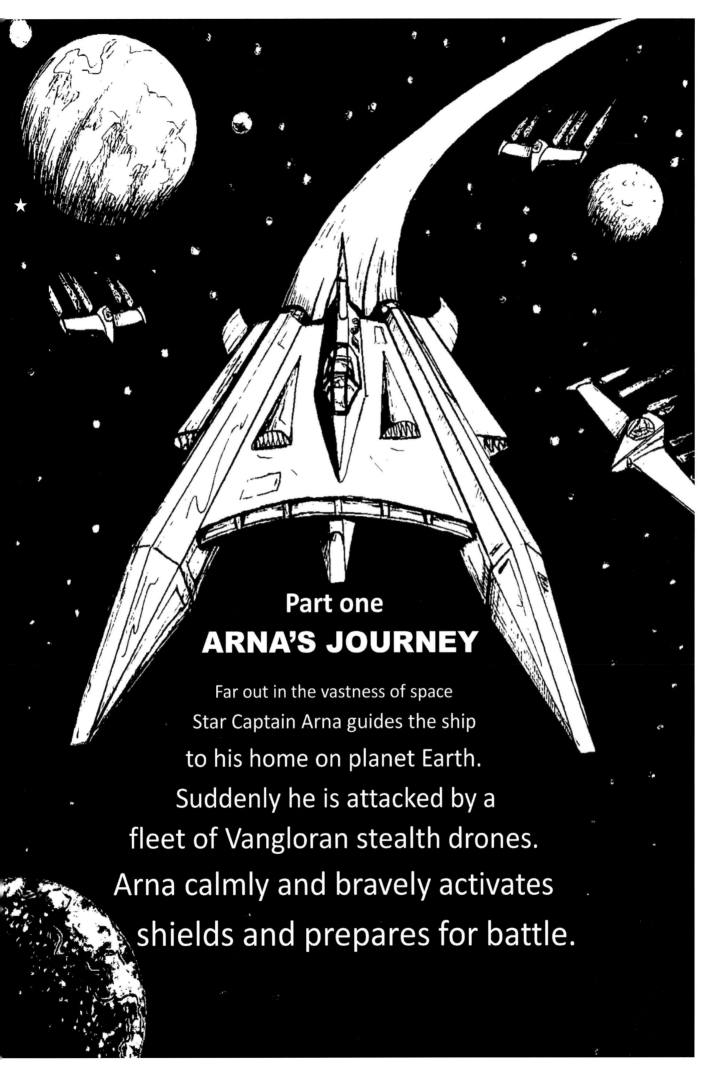

Part one
ARNA'S JOURNEY

Far out in the vastness of space
Star Captain Arna guides the ship
to his home on planet Earth.
Suddenly he is attacked by a
fleet of Vangloran stealth drones.
Arna calmly and bravely activates
shields and prepares for battle.

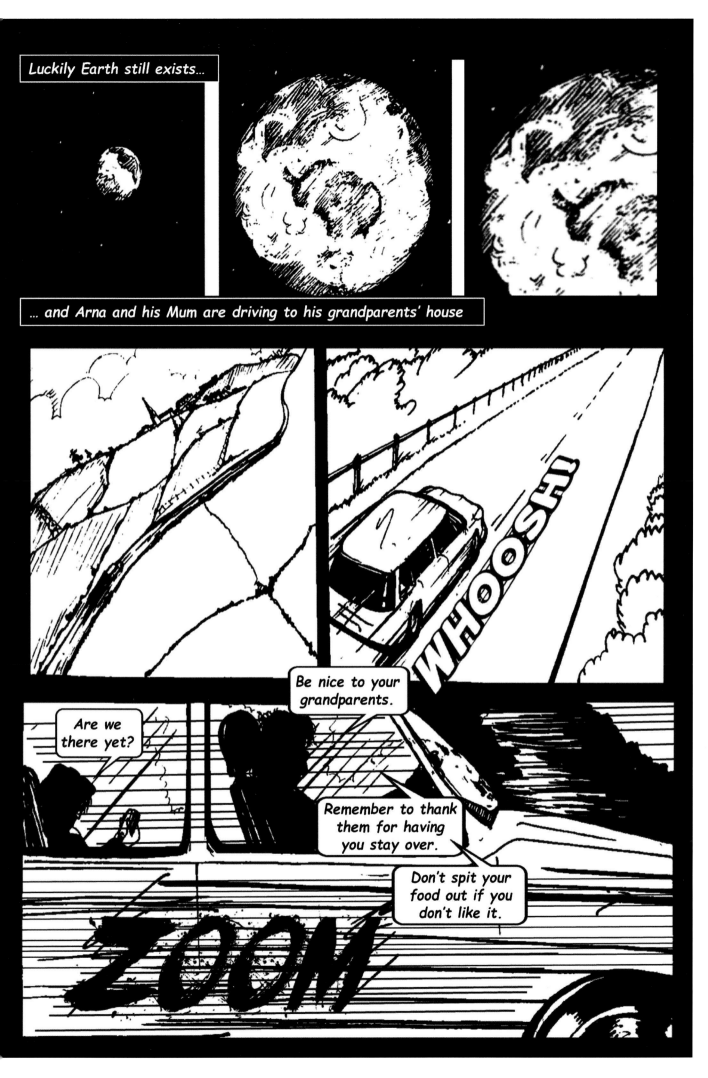

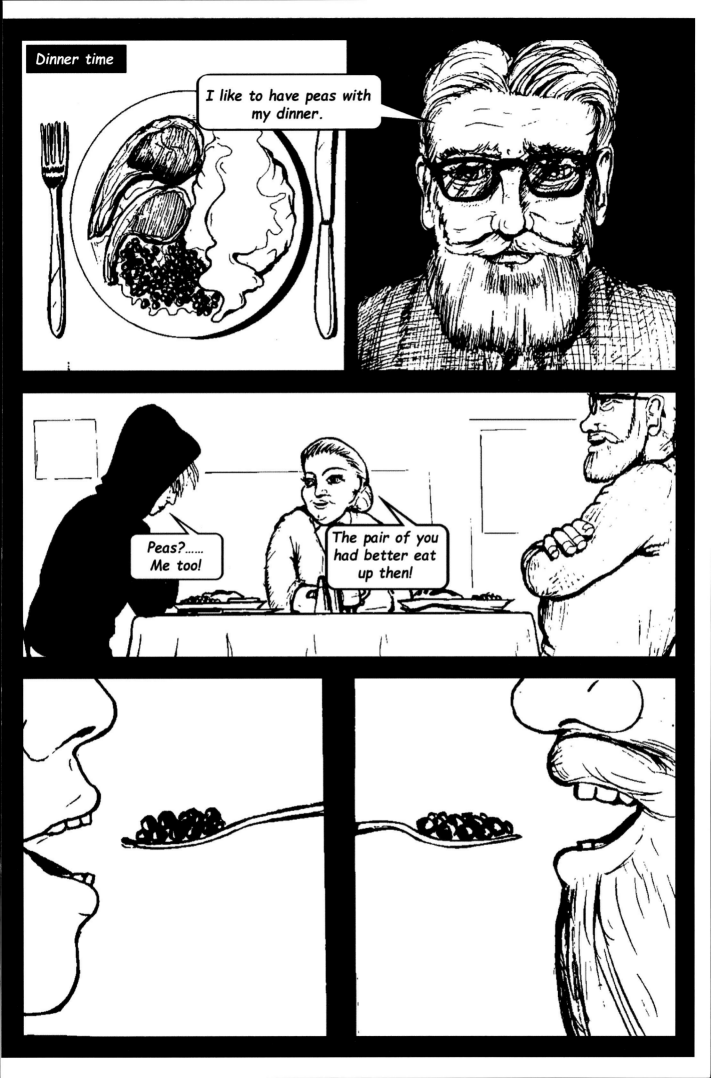

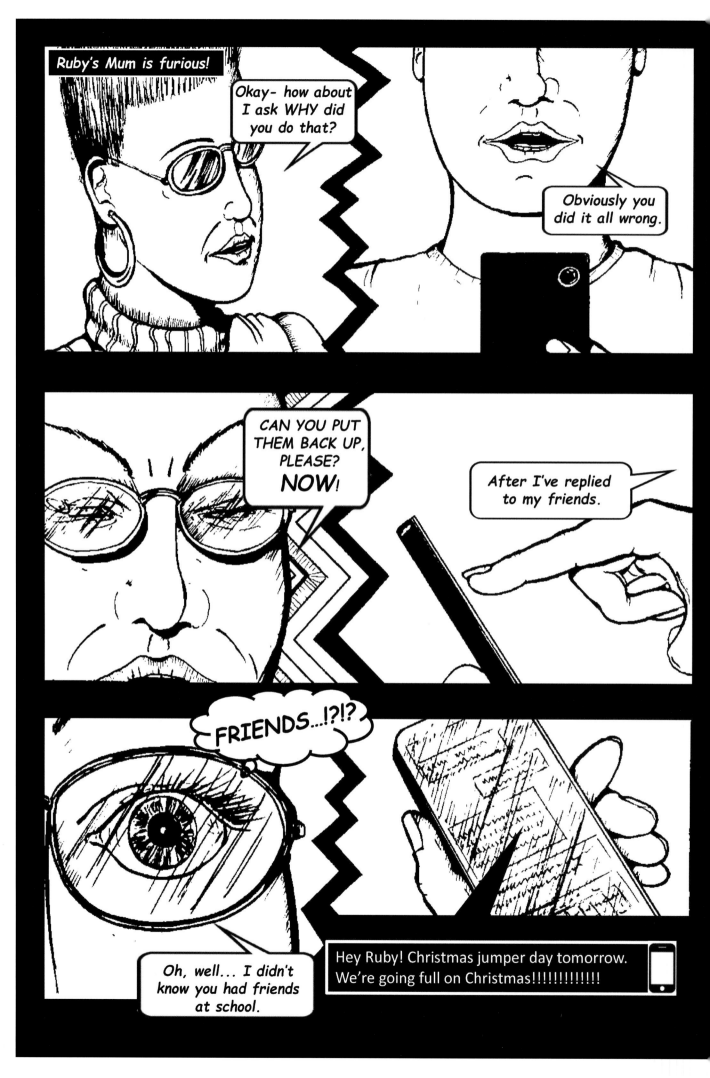

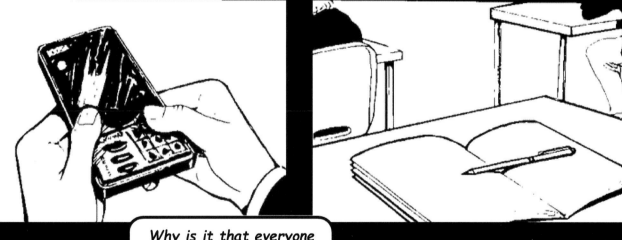

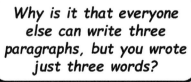

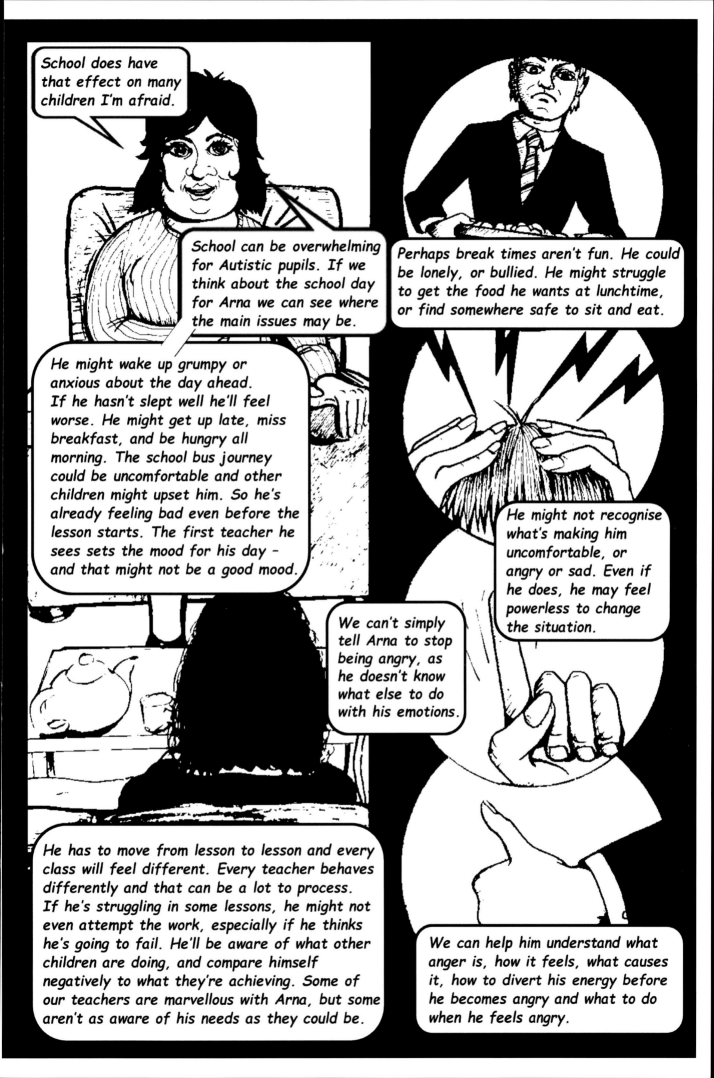

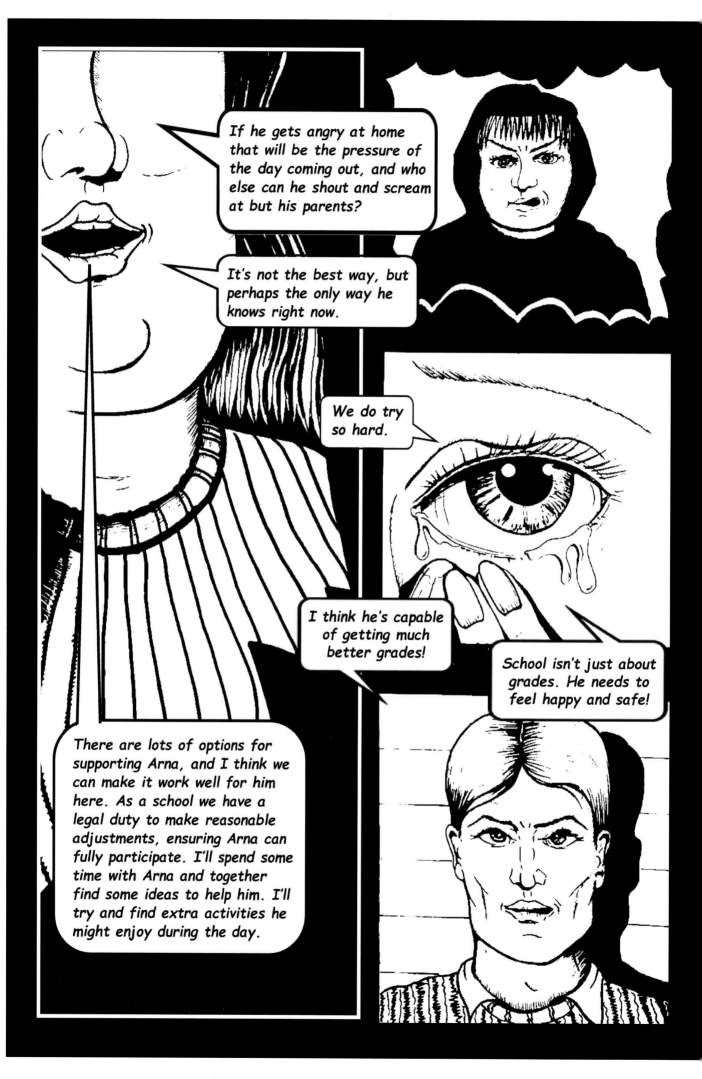

Support ideas
- Flexi hours
- Lunchtime clubs
- Adjusted timetable
- Movement breaks
- Personalised support
- Reduced homework
- Trips / visits support
- Fiddle toys / doodling
- Autism Mentor
- Quieter entrance
- Safe spaces
- Wellbeing sessions
- Friendship support
- and … … …

Hobbies and interests can be really important for Autistic people. They can be a good distraction, something to hyper-focus on and a source of immense pleasure. They can lead to opportunities, clubs and even careers.

We can help them develop their interests to become a little wider or healthier if needed. If a child is spending too long playing one game online we can introduce them to other games, and then perhaps some coding, or online game development courses.

Friendship doesn't mean the same thing to everyone. For some Autistic children having online friends works well, others may enjoy lots of socialising, some may have just one very special friend.
We can support both Autistic and non-Autistic children to behave appropriately with each other and learn what a positive relationship is. Talking about positive relationships can include how to offer and also to receive appropriate physical contact; kindness and fairness; sharing and showing an interest in other people's hobbies and lives. These things should go both ways in a friendship.

If they are obsessing about one animal, they could learn about where that animal lives, what it eats, similar animals ….

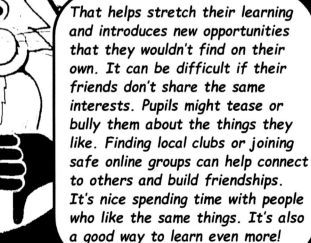

Schools should teach all staff and children about Autism, then they can all better understand how to help. They will appreciate that Autistic children may respond differently to them and worry about different things, but this doesn't mean they should be teased or excluded from games and groups.

That helps stretch their learning and introduces new opportunities that they wouldn't find on their own. It can be difficult if their friends don't share the same interests. Pupils might tease or bully them about the things they like. Finding local clubs or joining safe online groups can help connect to others and build friendships.
It's nice spending time with people who like the same things. It's also a good way to learn even more!

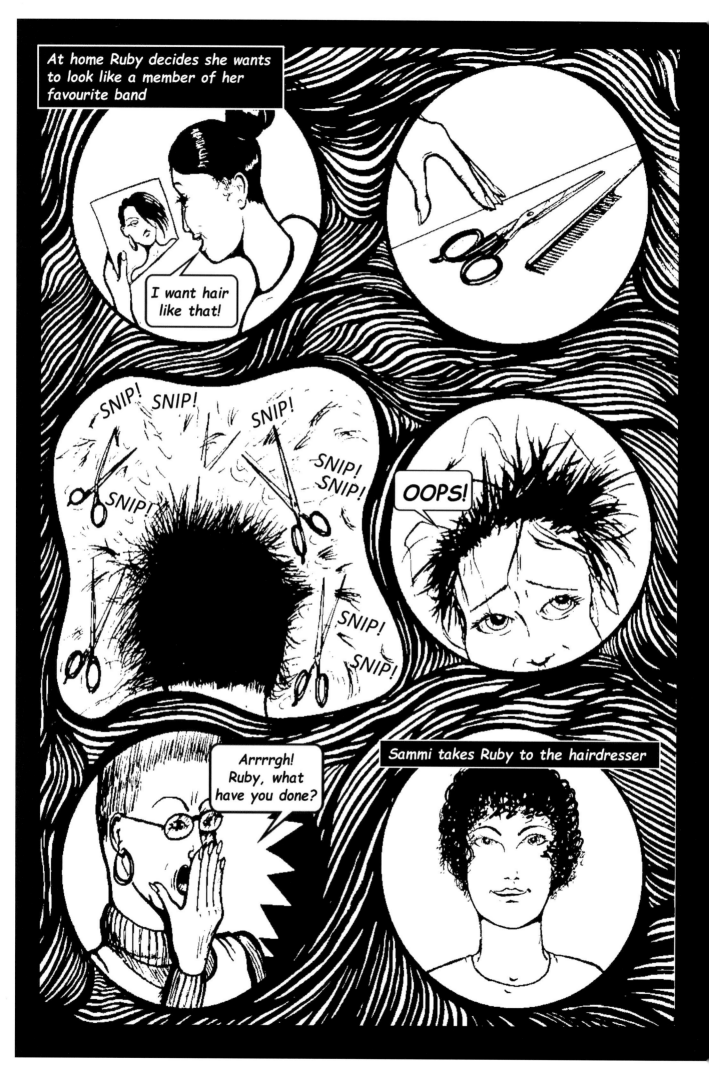

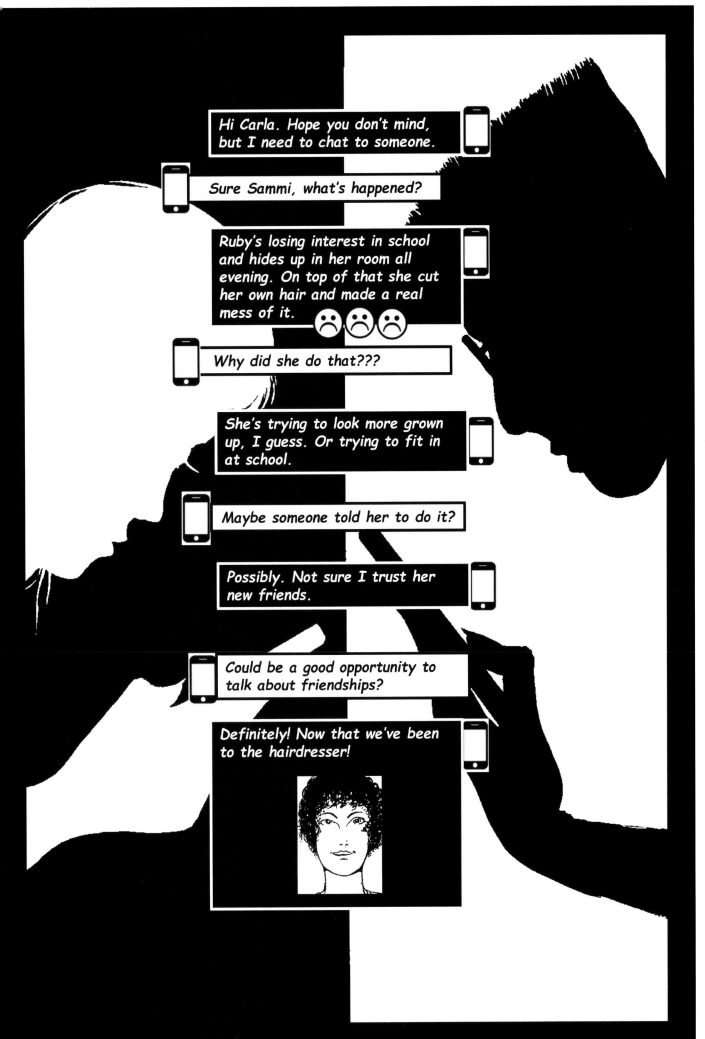

WELCOME

Online
Parent Information Evening

- **Common strengths and challenges**
- **Understanding and empathy**
- **How to help**

What is Autism?

At lunchtime Arna is eating his favourite food and wearing noise cancelling headphones